Proudly Presented To:

Your smile makes the world a happier place.

Love Always,

Date:

For my Mom & Dad,
who gave me a childhood full of happy memories and the confidence to follow my dreams.

All my love,
L.M.

For Grandma & Grandpa,
thanks for always believing in me.

Love you more,
C.B.

Printed in the USA
Published by Heartsong Press ™

Baby Tooth

Written by

LINDSEY MONTES DE OCA

Illustrated by

CHRISTY BERGERSON

From the moment your parents first saw your face,
you took a space in their hearts that no one else could replace.

When you were a baby, the whole world was brand new.

So your parents worked around the clock to feed, love, and take care of you.

Those newborn days brought many sleepless nights,
but they were also filled with heartwarming delights.

Despite the many hours of lost sleep,
it was worth every second for all of the
precious memories they'll keep.

Weeks passed in a whirl and after awhile...
one unsuspecting day you flashed your very first smile!

Pink and gummy and irresistible to all...
the more that you smiled, the more for you they'd fall.

Your family would do anything
to get a giggle or smile
from you.

They'd sing lullabies,
tickle your toes,
and play peek-a-boo!

As months passed, you started putting everything
in your mouth to bite and chew.
Though it sounds funny now, that's how you
discovered the world around you.

Then one unsuspecting day your happy face
became red and seething.
"Uh-oh!" thought your parents, "Here comes the teething!"

I'm sorry for all of
the pain it caused you.

I just couldn’t figure out
how to break through!

Finally I got it right and proudly made my debut.
I was so excited to start my adventure with you.

I arrived just in time for you to start eating solid food.
Now we can have a banquet whenever we're in the mood!

But that was just the start of our fun.
More of us happily settled in by the time you turned one.

You quickly went from crawling to toddling to walking.
And it was amazing to hear your babbling turn into talking.

When you finally uttered your very first word,
it was the sweetest thing that we had ever heard!

It was exciting for everyone to hear what was on your mind.
After the first few words, they started coming in bursts of all kind.

Say Mama!

Say Dada!

DOGGY!

Say Hi!

Say Gammy!

The toddler years
were busy and
went by in a flash.

Your parents
chased you around
the house in a
never-ending dash.

In the blink of an eye you went
from a tricycle, to training
wheels, onto a two wheel bike.

When you practice and put
your mind to it,
you can do anything you like!

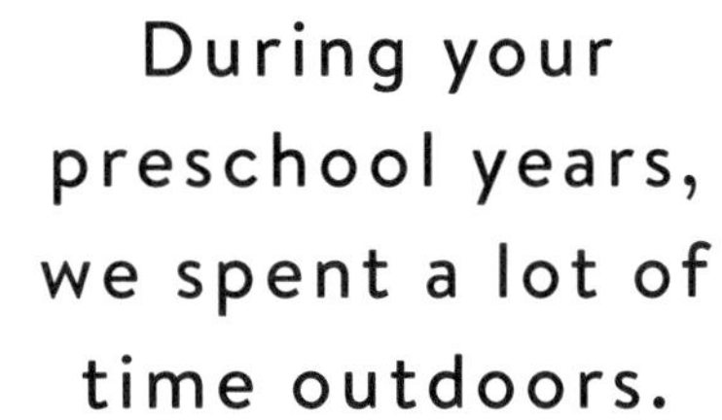

During your
preschool years,
we spent a lot of
time outdoors.

We especially loved
swimming, camping and
making s'mores.

We spent sunny days
blowing bubbles and
making dandelion wishes,

and nights
reading bedtime
books and sharing
butterfly kisses.

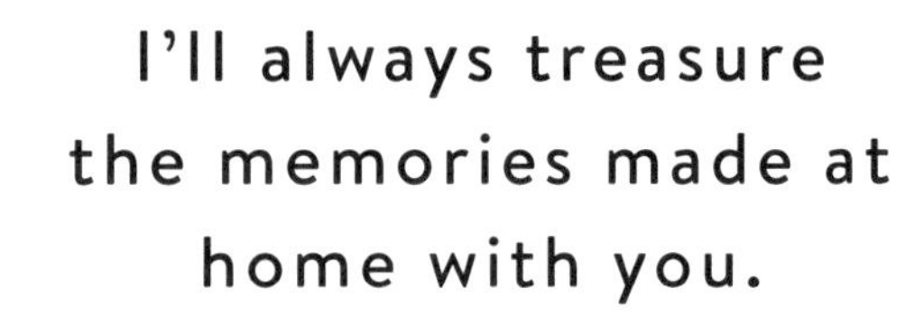

I'll always treasure
the memories made at
home with you.

With dress up and
our imaginations,
there's nothing we can't do!

I feel so lucky that I can go with
you to school!
I get to stay with you until
kindergarten, as a general rule.

Each baby tooth moves out at a different pace.
There's no need to be sad, because Forever Tooth will come in my place.

Forever Tooth is strong, loving, and wise...
grown up and fun, the coolest tooth there is, in my eyes.

When I first came to you, I came to you knowing
that once you were old enough, I'd have to get going.

You can see how much you've grown when you look in the mirror,
which is why it's time for Forever Tooth to come here.

Your hands, feet, and body
have all grown much taller
and your mouth hasn't
gotten any smaller!

You'll need bigger teeth because you will continue to grow,
which is why I know it's almost my time to go.

Falling out is much easier
for us than it was getting in.
Every baby tooth has a
tune that makes him
wiggle and grin.

We each hear music that makes our
heart dance. It causes us to shimmy and
shake like we have ants in our pants!

Some samba, some waltz, while
others prefer hip-hop.
Jazz, disco, or country…once the
beat starts, we just can't stop.

Listening to the song in our
hearts moves us on to our
life's next stage, just as you
must listen to your heart to
guide you as you age.

Place me in a pillow, along with a letter, for the Tooth Fairy,
and I will get to see what great plans she has for me!

Letting me go is a very “big kid” thing to do.
It will be sad to say goodbye but
I’ll always cherish my time with you.

Luckily
your parents
took a million
photos of me

so you can look
back at our time
together with glee.

Growing up is a journey and your future looks so bright.
Remember to work hard, be kind, and do what is right.

Your big smile and happy heart bring joy to those around you.
The more you share them with the world, the more your dreams will come true.

Made in United States
Troutdale, OR
11/10/2023

14465608R00024